PUG SOLVES A PROBLEM

Empower Children to Become
Problem Solvers

Written & Illustrated by Lindsey Kealey

PAWsitive
Choices ®

This book is lovingly dedicated to Chancho,
the amazing pug who inspired this story.

Text and illustrations © 2014-2021 PAWsitive Choices, LLC
First print edition 2021

Kealey, Lindsey-author, illustrator
Pug Solves a Problem/Lindsey Kealey

ISBN 978-1-7357367-3-0

Published by PAWsitive Choices, LLC
Bend, OR, USA

What is PAWsitive Choices?

PAWsitive Choices Social & Emotional Learning is an easy-to-use guide for teachers and families that teaches social and emotional learning skills through engaging stories. Research-based strategies are interwoven throughout the curriculum to support optimal brain development and help children thrive.

PAWsitive Choices teaches you how to:

* Solve problems
* Learn from mistakes
* Set goals
* Make positive choices
* Talk about feelings
* Listen and think
* Make healthy choices
* Take brain breaks
* Take calming breaths
* Use positive self-talk

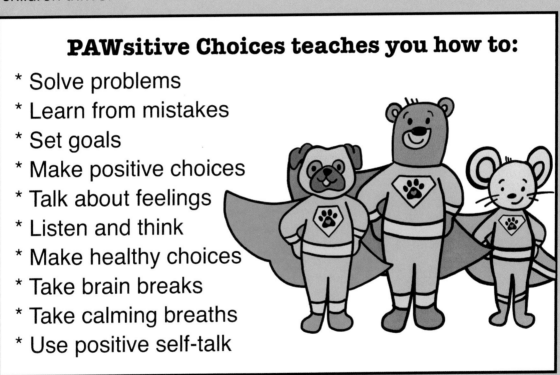

Visit pawsitivechoices.com to check out our complete curriculum.

This book teaches problem solving skills through the story of Pug and his family. You can download and print the **Problem Solving Reflection** to help children process problems, learn from mistakes, and repair relationships. Put the reflection in a page protector and use a dry-erase marker to make it reusable and make copies so each child has their own reflection form. To watch videos and download other exclusive resources visit:

https://www.pawsitivechoices.com/pugsolvesaproblemresources

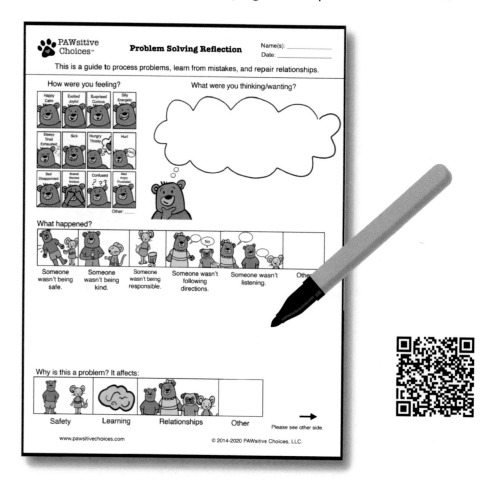

A Note to Grown-Ups: Problem Solving Basics

PAWsitive Choices uses a research-based approach to problem solving with children. Using the Problem Solving Reflection is a productive process because the goal is to learn from problems.

Productive

Punitive

A punitive approach to solving problems often focuses on the unwanted behavior and assigning a punishment. On the other hand, productive problem solving helps you understand feelings, thoughts, and needs behind the behavior and lets you find a way to repair relationships. A punitive process perpetuates shame. By contrast, a productive process encourages empathy and creates accountability.

To learn more about problem solving, discipline, emotional regulation, and other topics, listen to The PAWsitive Choices Podcast!

One day at school, Pug learned something amazing …

He learned his brain has problem solving powers!

"Every time you solve a problem, your brain gets stronger. This strengthens your problem solving superpowers!" said Teacher Bear.

That day, Pug, Bear, and Mouse practiced these powers.
Some problems, they solved by themselves.

Breathe Power

Walk Away Power

Ignore Power

Brain Break Power

Other problems, they solved together.

Talk it Out Power

I feel …

Say Sorry Power

I'm sorry.

Share Power

Ask for Help Power

At the end of the day, Teacher Bear taught the class about the Problem Solving Reflection.

This helps you think about a problem, find a way to solve it, and make a plan for next time.

Pug came home from school and ate a healthy snack.

He started to read his sister's book.

When Pug's sister saw him reading, her smile turned into a frown.

Hey, that's MY book! Why do you always take my things?!

 Watch this video to learn about a "mixed up brain."

"I know just what we need!" exclaimed Pug.

Pug and his sister took three calming breaths together.

Watch this video to learn different calming breaths.

"First, you reflect. This means to think about what happened. How were you feeling? What were you thinking? Did you want something?" asked Pug. Sister drew and wrote about her thoughts and feelings.

"Now, think about what happened," said Pug. Sister paused and then wrote and drew some more.

What happened?

| Someone wasn't being safe. | Someone wasn't being kind. | Someone wasn't being responsible. | Someone wasn't following directions. | Someone wasn't listening. |

I got mad when I saw Pug with my book. My brain felt mixed up and I yelled at him. He felt sad.

21

"What positive choice do you want to make next time?" asked Pug. "I want to be kind to you, even when I feel mad," answered Sister. "Which problem solving powers can you use?" asked Pug. "I can use breathe power and talk it out power," said Sister. "Next time, I'll ask you *before* I use one of your things," added Pug.

"The last thing you do is find a solution," explained Pug. Sister looked at the ideas on the page and circled a solution. "I'm sorry for yelling at you. Next time, I will breathe and talk to you kindly." Pug replied, "I forgive you. Let's have a redo!"

What can you do to solve the problem?

Talk it out. Apologize. Make a sorry letter. Do something kind. Clean up the mess. Have a redo.

"A redo is when you do something over again, but *this* time, you make a positive choice and use a problem solving power," explained Pug. "Let's do it!" said Sister.

Review Questions

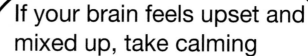

If your brain feels upset and mixed up, take calming

_____
(breaths)

When was a time you had a problem? What happened?

What problem solving powers do you want to use?

PAWsitive Choices™ Problem Solving Powers

Breathe Power

Brain Break Power

Take Turns Power

Share Power

Ignore Power

Please Stop Power

Walk Away Power

Talk it Out Power

Say Sorry Power

Problem Solve Power

Ask for Help Power

www.pawsitivechoices.com

A Note to Grown-Ups: Problem Solving Resources

You can download and print the **Problem Solving Reflection,** Problem Solving Powers Poster, Apology Letter Template, and other exclusive resources by visiting:

pawsitivechoices.com/pugsolvesaproblemresources

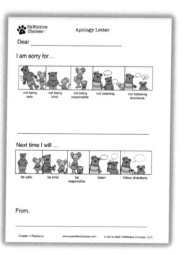

About the Author

Lindsey Kealey is a university instructor of education, speaker, coach, and creator of PAWsitive Choices Social and Emotional Learning. She earned a Bachelor of Science in Human Development and Family Sciences with an emphasis in child development and holds a Master of Arts in Teaching. Her university work, as well as her experience teaching in public schools, helped her craft a trauma-informed curriculum that integrates neuroscience, social and emotional learning, and problem solving into a program that helps children thrive. A California native, she now lives in Central Oregon and enjoys exploring the outdoors with her family and pug.

For more information about PAWsitive Choices curriculum, trainings, and events, visit www.pawsitivechoices.com or send an email to info@pawsitivechoices.com.

Visit our store to check out more books and products!

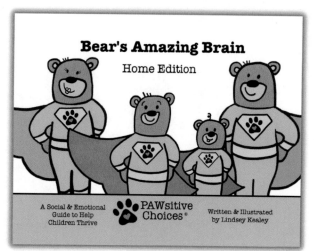

www.pawsitivechoices.com/store

More adventures coming soon!

Made in the USA
Middletown, DE
04 December 2021

53685648R00020